MAKE NO LITTLE PLANS; THEY HAVE NO MAGIC TO STIR MEN'S BLOOD AND PROBABLY THEMSELVES WILL NOT BE REALIZED. MAKE BIG PLANS...

Daniel Burnham

Copyright © 2020 by Aleksandr D. Vaysman

Library of Congress United States Copyright Office
Registration Number - TXu 2-182-646

All rights reserved.

No part of this publication may be reproduced, stored in a retrieval system, or transmitted in any form or by any means, electronic, mechanical, photocopying, recording, or otherwise, without written permission of the publisher - ADV. This book is a work of fiction. Names, characters, places, and incidents are either the product of Author's imagination or are used fictitiously, and any resemblance to actual persons, living or dead, business establishments, events, or locales is entirely coincidental.

ISBN 978-1-7346029-0-6
This edition first printing, June 2020

The illustrations are by German Verona - "Wallok"

www.alexvaysman.com

Little Misha in BIG America

Written by Alex Vaysman
Illustrated by Wallok

To my grandparents and parents who brought us here -
M.M.☒.C.
I think of you every day.

02.11.1992 - 9 of us arrived in the USA.
M.M.☒.C.A.☒.☒.A.☒.

To my amazing wife, my boys and my princess -
A.J.B.I.
I don't need the whole world to love me, I just need you to.

Thank you.

Little Misha, his cat Tisha,
　Mama Anna and Papa Grisha -
Gathered all in the yard
　　We just got our **GREEN** card!
And without delay -
　　　Time for us to **DEPART!**

Need to pack my favorite toys,
Give the rest to girls and boys -
I WILL SEE YOU ALL AGAIN!
You can play with them till then.

Red cars, blue cars, large cars, small cars,
People sitting, people walking,
some are quiet, some are talking.
Today from home we took a taxi,
But usually we take a bus.
We just arrived at an **AIRPORT** -
Cat Tisha is also with us!

To the baggage claim we go,
 NUMBER 9 that's us, we made it!
Misha climbs on top of suitcases
 And yells out, We **IMMIGRATED!**

CAN'T wait to write home
about my new home.
CAN'T wait to tell friends
about my new friends.
CAN'T wait to show **MOM**
how much I can learn,
CAN'T wait to help **DAD**
assemble my bed!

NEW school and new teachers,
NEW pencils and notebooks,
NEW sports with huge bleachers,
NEW ways
to do homework.

So much I don't know,
So hard to keep up,
So many new things.
Misha thought to **GIVE UP**.

Oh Mommy and Daddy, I want to go **BACK**.
I want my old toys and I want my old bed.
I want things the same as things **USED** to be,
I want my old **ROOM**, I wish I could **FLEE!**

It's hard to imagine how much you give up,
So you can live better,
to get a fresh start.
A place that you once considered a **HOME**,
A place you once **LOVED**
where you felt you belonged.

With time Misha felt the **UNCERTAINTY** fade.
With time he grew stronger, no longer afraid.
He made many friends, learned new sports, loved his teachers.
He joined different clubs and discovered new features.

NEW country gave Misha so many abilities,
So many **NEW** choices with new possibilities.
The world became smaller with different discoveries,
With **NEW** opportunities, exploring new qualities.

It's very important to feel you belong,
To feel you're protected and **LOVED** all along.
A home is a feeling of safety and trust,
To learn from mistakes, to grow, readjust.

CPSIA information can be obtained
at www.ICGtesting.com
Printed in the USA
LVHW070045280820
664251LV00022B/1166

9 781734 602906